Enid Blyton's™

NODDY™

annual 1995

CONSULTANT EDITOR Gillian Baverstock   **EDUCATIONAL ADVISOR** Godfrey Hall
NEW ILLUSTRATIONS Andrew Geeson

Original Text and Images copyright © Darrell Waters Ltd. 1949/68. Text and Images of BBC Television Series
copyright © BBC Enterprises Ltd. 1992. Licensed by BBC Enterprises Ltd. All rights reserved.
Published in Great Britain by World International, an imprint of Egmont Publishing Ltd., Egmont House,
PO Box 111, Great Ducie Street, Manchester M60 3BL.
Printed in Italy. ISBN 0 7498 1991 X
"NODDY" is a trademark of Darrell Waters Ltd., and is used under licence.
"Enid Blyton" (signature logotype) is a trademark of Darrell Waters Ltd., and is used under licence.

£4.99
UK only

CONTENTS

TOY TOWN SCHOOL NOTE FOR GROWN-UPS
The "Toy Town School" pages have been designed to develop children's progress through the early stages of the National Curriculum.
Most activities lead towards Levels 1 and 2.

A Letter from Noddy

Hello boys and girls!

I'm little Noddy. You all know me, don't you? I've got a nodding head, that's why I'm called Noddy. If you tap it, it nods faster than ever. Would you like a head like that? I like mine.

I hope you like my Annual. It has all kinds of stories and pictures, and I keep finding myself in them. I always look for my little blue cap with the bell, and I wish it would tinkle in the pictures, but it doesn't.

I've a friend called Big-Ears. He's a good friend because he always helps me when I get into trouble. He's a brownie, and he lives in a toadstool house up in the woods. He's got a bicycle and he has a little cart to fit behind it. I've got a little car and I wash and polish it every day. I take the toys for rides to the station, or anywhere they want to go, and they pay me sixpence a time. It's fun to be a taxi-driver. Will you let me take you in my car if you come to Toy Town, please?

I live in a little house made of toy bricks, just like the ones you have in your toybox. All the people who live with me in Toy Town are in my Annual. There is Tessie Bear and Bumpy Dog, and Mr Jumbo and the Wobbly Man, and the Tubby Bears and Mr Plod, and . . . well I can't remember them all!

Let me know if you come to Toy Town and I will be sure to meet you at the station in my little car. And I won't charge you sixpence – it will only be a *penny* for you, because I shall be *so* pleased to see you.

Lots of love from

Noddy

Hello

Hello, Hello
Does anybody
Want some help
From little Noddy?

Parcels fetched
And shopping done
Letters posted
Errands run.

Windows cleaned
And doorsteps too,
Goods delivered
All day through!

If you're wanting
Cakes for tea
Or eggs for supper,
Shout for ME!

Noddy and the Fire-Engine

One afternoon, when Noddy was driving slowly through Toy Town, he noticed a very peculiar thing.

A little house stood back from the road with a nice garden in front – and out of one of the upstairs windows was coming a thin spiral of smoke. Noddy stared at it as he drove by. Why should smoke come out of a *window*? Hadn't the house got any chimneys? Yes, it had four! Then why did the smoke come out of a window?

"I wonder – I just *wonder* – if there's something on fire there!" said Noddy, and he suddenly felt excited and his bell rang loudly on his hat. "Perhaps I'd better knock at the door and ask if everything is all right."

So he drove back to the gate of the pretty little house. He got out of his car and went up the garden path. He knocked loudly at the blue front door and rang the bell. Rat-a-tat-tat! Jingle-jing! Nobody came to the door, so Noddy went round the back. The kitchen door was locked and he

couldn't make anyone hear – nor could he get in. Then he saw a little note on the doorstep. "No bread today. Back tomorrow."

"Oh – the people have gone away!" said Noddy. "NOW what shall I do? I really must find out if something is on fire."

He went round to the front again, and saw that a tree grew right up to the window out of which the smoke was drifting.

"I'd better climb it," said Noddy. "It doesn't look a very hard tree to climb."

So up he went and looked in at the window, which was shut except for a little crack at the top.

Goodness – what a shock he had! A fire had been left burning in the room, and a piece of coal had jumped out on to the rug and was burning!

"Fire!" shouted Noddy, and almost fell out of the tree. "Fetch the fire-engine, quick! The rug's burning – and now the flame has reached a little table and one leg's burning! Fire!"

Oh dear, oh dear – the flames were now burning all the table, and a waste paper basket, too – and soon they would reach the book-shelf and what a blaze there would be then!

"I must go to the fire station and tell the firemen," thought Noddy. "Yes, that's what I must do."

So he slid down the tree and got into his car. Away he went, hooting madly to make everyone get out of his way quickly. Mr Plod saw him flash by and

was very cross.

"Going along at fifty miles an hour!" said Mr Plod. "I'll have something to say to you about this, Noddy."

Noddy arrived at the fire station – but alas, the fire-engine wasn't there, nor were there any firemen to be seen.

"Where is everybody?" yelled Noddy. "Fire, fire!"

A small doll shouted back to Noddy.

"They've taken the fire-engine to put out a fire on Farmer Straw's farm."

"Oh, goodness me!" said Noddy and raced his car up to the farm. Ah – there was the fire-engine standing quietly in the lane. The fire had been put out – but where were the firemen? Not one was to be seen!

"Fire! Fire!" shouted Noddy. The firemen were all down at the farm-house having some lemonade and cakes with the farmer and his wife. One put his head out of the door when he heard Noddy's shout. He put it back again, laughing heartily.

"It's only little Noddy! He's seen our fire-engine and he's got all excited. He's shouting 'Fire! Fire!' as if there really was one here!"

Noddy was very worried indeed. He couldn't *think* where the firemen had gone to. What was he to do?

"That dear little house will be all burnt

down if I go to look for the firemen," he thought. "Oh – I wonder now – I do, do wonder – if I could drive that fire-engine!"

He slid out of his little car and ran to the gleaming fire-engine. He climbed into the driving seat. Now – here was the steering-wheel – and there was the thing that started up the engine – and that must be the brake. He could only *just* reach it because his legs were so short.

R-r-r-r-r-r-r! He started up the engine – it moved off down the lane. Ooooooh! What a thrill for Noddy! His head nodded madly and his face went very red.

The fire-bell rang as he went along – and when he came into Toy Town everyone ran out to see the fire-engine, Mr Plod, too. He stared with his mouth wide open at the surprising sight of *Noddy* driving the fire-engine!

"What next?" he said. "What next?" And he jumped on his bicycle and raced after Noddy.

Noddy came to the house where the fire was, and stopped the fire-engine. Dear me, there was a *great* deal of smoke coming out of the window now – and was that a flame?

Noddy leapt down and wondered how to get the hose and the water to the house. What did firemen do next? But he didn't have to wonder long because Mr Plod arrived on his bicycle, red in the face with anger.

"What do you mean by this, little Noddy?" he roared – and then he suddenly saw all the thick smoke coming out of the window.

"See – it's on fire!" shouted Noddy. "I found the fire-engine but I couldn't see the firemen – so I brought the engine here myself, Mr Plod. How do we get the water to put out the fire?"

Well, Mr Plod knew all about things like that, of course! A lot of people had come running up now, and he gave his orders quickly. "You, Mr Tubby Bear, find the water under that iron grating there – take up the lid, that's right. And you, Mr Toy Dog, fasten the end of that hose to the tap down there.

Turn on the water when I tell you! Hey, Mr Noah, help me to run the hose into the garden."

Noddy climbed the tree and looked in at the window. "Everything's burning!" he cried. "Bring the hose up here, Mr Plod." He pulled up the hose himself, and then Mr Tubby Bear climbed up beside him, and soon the

water was pouring into the burning room, making a hissing, sizzling noise.

"Hurray!" shouted everyone. "Hurray! The fire will soon be out!"

"It's OUT!" shouted Noddy. "Nothing but smoke left."

"Come on down, Noddy," said Mr Plod, and Noddy climbed down, keeping as far away from Mr Plod as he could. But the policeman grabbed hold of him – and will you believe it, he set little Noddy on his shoulders and carried him all the way through Toy Town like that.

"Here comes Noddy, who saved a house from burning down!" he shouted. "Here comes Noddy, who drove the fire-engine all by himself – though he mustn't do it again unless he asks me. Here comes Noddy, so give him a cheer!"

And you should have heard the loud hurrays all the way down the street.

Big-Ears couldn't *think* what was going on when he came riding through on his bicycle.

When he saw Noddy being carried on Mr Plod's shoulders he was so astonished that he fell off his bicycle – bump!

"Noddy! What are you doing up there? Noddy, why are you so dirty, why is your face so black? Noddy why…"

You wait a little, Big-Ears, and hear Noddy answer your questions. You really WILL be surprised!

Noddy Says!

How much do you remember? Give yourself a nod for each answer you get right.

- Why did Noddy climb the tree?
- What did Noddy see through the window of the little house?
- Where were the firemen?
- Who helped Noddy put out the fire?

Toy Town School
with Miss Prim

Learn about being brave

Something to know

In the story 'Noddy and the Fire-Engine' Noddy came across a fire during a drive through Toy Town. Fires start very easily and it is very important that you NEVER play with matches or play near a fire. An open fire should always have a guard in front of it in case something hot jumps out on to the carpet.

Something to understand

Noddy was very brave in the story and had to decide what to do. Sometimes when there is no one else around we have to decide for ourselves what we must do. In the story Noddy decided that he must get the fire-engine otherwise the house might burn down. Do you think he did the right thing?

If there is a fire and you need to get help you dial 999 for the fire brigade. They will come quickly with a bright red fire-engine fitted with special equipment to help put out the fire. Remember, fires are very dangerous.

Something to do

You will need a grown-up to help you with this.

In the story certain people helped Noddy. See if you can remember which ones helped him. What did they do? Where were the fire-fighters?

Mr Toy Dog
Mr Plod
Mr Tubby Bear
Big-Ears
Farmer Straw

MISS PRIM'S NOTE FOR GROWN-UPS

It is very important to discuss with children what to do in case of an accident or a fire. They need to be aware of the dangers at home and outside. Children should have the opportunity to talk about the story and discuss what happened. Talking and listening are important parts of the National Curriculum. They should be able to remember the main characters in the story and the basic plot.

It does not take very much for a fire to start. A hot coal on a carpet or a dropped match is enough. Once a fire has started it will spread very quickly. Some things burn very easily, like paper and clothes.

One of the most dangerous things about a fire is the smoke. It is important if there is a fire to keep doors shut to stop the smoke from spreading. When fire-fighters go into burning houses they wear special masks to help them breathe.

Draw a circle round the things that Noddy might have used to help put out the fire.

The Skittles' Tea Party

1 Noddy took Mrs Skittle out shopping with her big basket.

2 "I am giving the children a tea party today," she told Noddy.

3 "That is why I have bought so many cakes and balloons."

4 Noddy drove her home, and helped her in with the parcels.

5 "The children are out playing!" said Mrs Skittle.

6 "Ring my bell for them, Noddy." But the bell was broken!

7 "Oh dear – I shall never get the children in," said Mrs Skittle.

8 Noddy took off his hat, and he started shaking it about.

9 The children heard the bell on Noddy's hat. They soon came in!

Toy Town School
with Miss Prim

Learn about cooking

Something to know

Mrs Skittle was having a tea party and so she wanted to buy something special. During the year there are particular days when we cook special cakes or buns. On birthdays and at Christmas we bake special cakes and on Good Friday we eat Hot Cross Buns. What kinds of cake do you like best?

Something to understand

It is great fun to make your own cake. When you cook something you change the way it looks and feels. The flour, butter, milk and eggs are soft when they are in the bowl. After they have been cooked they are very different. Food changes when it is cooked.

MISS PRIM'S NOTES FOR GROWN-UPS

On these pages there are two safe recipes that can be tried out. Cooking and changes of state are an important part of the Science Curriculum. Recipes are an important part of Mathematics in the areas of measurement and counting. Talk to your children about the kind of things they like eating and drinking and discuss with them what kind of changes take place if you cook something.

Something to do

Mrs Skittle was having a special tea party for her children. Draw in the space below some things that Big-Ears, Tessie Bear and Tubby Bear might have had for **their** tea.

Some things to make

Here are some delicious things made by Tessie Bear and Noddy for a special party.

Tessie Bear's Sandwiches

You will need
4 slices of bread
butter
cream cheese
chopped apple
knife   bowl

Butter two slices of bread. Mix the cream cheese and the pieces of apple in a bowl. Spread the mixture on the two slices of bread and put the other slices on top. Ask a grown-up to cut up the sandwiches. Tessie Bear also likes to try cream cheese and pineapple on her sandwiches.

Noddy's Fruity Dip

You will need
4 heaped tablespoons of
    natural plain yogurt
4 heaped tablespoons of fromage frais
an apple, peach and pear
1 level tablespoon of caster sugar
bowl   spoon   knife   tablespoon

Put the fromage frais and yogurt into a bowl and mix it well. Add the sugar. Wash the fruit. Ask a grown-up to cut up the fruit. Add this to the bowl. Noddy enjoys serving his fruity dip in small dishes and decorating the top with pieces of fruit. He sometimes tries other fruits such as strawberries.

Remember!
- Make sure you wash your hands before you start.
- Be careful with knives.
- Always make sure a grown-up helps you.
- Clear away after you have finished.

Noddy and the Kite

It is a very windy day. Tessie and Noddy are going to fly a kite in Mr Straw's field. Tessie puts her basket of eggs on top of the milk churn ready for Mr Milko to collect.

"Hurry, Tessie!" calls Noddy. "This kite is longing to fly!"

The kite flies very high because the wind is so strong and Noddy and Tessie have to hold the string tightly. After a time they are hungry. Noddy ties the kite to the milk churn while they have a picnic in the sunshine.

The wind blows harder than ever. Suddenly, the kite sails high in the air, pulling the milk churn behind it, with Tessie's basket of eggs still on top.

"Stop! Stop!" cry Noddy and Tessie, jumping into the car to follow the kite.

In Toy Town, white puddles are falling from the sky. Mr Jumbo tastes one. "It's milk!" he says. Then eggs drop on to Mr Wobbly Man and Mr Jumbo. The toys cannot understand it.

Mr Plod slips on an egg. "Whatever is happening?" he asks.

"You slipped on a broken egg," says Mr Tubby.

"Milk and eggs are falling out of the sky," says Mr Wobbly Man.

"This is very serious," says Mr Plod. "I shall offer a reward of a bag of sixpences to anyone who can explain why it is raining like this."

Noddy and Tessie follow the kite for a long way. "We'll never catch up with it," says Noddy. But just at that moment, Tessie's basket falls into Noddy's arms. Then they see the milk churn rolling noisily towards them.

Noddy and Tessie drive into Toy Town with the milk churn in the back of the car. Mr Plod meets them and they explain what has happened. "So the milk churn and eggs must have flown over the market square and that's why it was raining milk and eggs!" says Mr Plod.

Mr Plod gives Noddy the reward for explaining the strange rain.

"First, I'll take back the churn to Mr Straw and pay for the milk," says Noddy. "Then I'll buy Tessie an ice-cream – and you can come too, Mr Plod," he adds, winking at Tessie Bear.

Toy Town School
with Miss Prim

Something to know

In the story the wind was blowing very hard. Sometimes a very strong wind can damage houses and blow down trees. This is called a gale. The wind is very powerful and if you are out in a strong wind it can be difficult to walk.

Something to understand

In the story something unexpected happened to Noddy when the milk churn and eggs were blown into the air. We cannot always tell what is going to happen next. It was a great surprise when it started raining eggs and milk. Can you think of something that has happened to you that you didn't expect? You may have had a surprise letter or visitor. Some surprises are fun but others such as eggs falling out of the sky are not so good.

MISS PRIM'S NOTE FOR GROWN-UPS

The weather is an important part of Geography and Science in the National Curriculum. Investigate with your children how hard the wind is blowing. Record the rainfall with them by using a yogurt pot in the garden and talk about how important the rain is to plants and flowers. Discuss with them different types of surprises.

Something to make

You will need
a plastic cup or a yogurt pot, card, a long stick

Ask a grown-up to cut two slits opposite each other in the side of the cup or yogurt pot. Poke a piece of card through the slits. It should stick out from each side of the cup. Push a long stick into the ground. Place your wind tester on the top of the stick. Watch how it moves when the wind blows. What happens to the card when the wind is blowing hard? I think Noddy could have done with a wind tester before he decided to fly his kite, don't you?

A Windy Day

It is such a windy day that Noddy, Big-Ears, Tessie Bear and Mr Milko have lost their hats. Draw a line to match the correct hat to each of them.

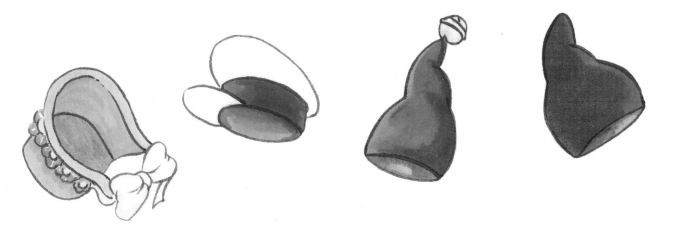

Crash! Bumpity-Bump!

One night Noddy went to fetch Mr Jumbo from the station, and take him home with all his luggage. So off he drove in good time to meet the train.

Chuffitty-chuffitty-chuff! There it was, puffing into the station. The driver waved to Noddy and he waved back. Then he looked for Mr Jumbo. Ah, he was just getting out of a carriage.

"Here I am, Mr Jumbo!"

cried Noddy. "I'll help you with your luggage."

The little porter helped too, and soon it was in the back of Noddy's car. Mr Jumbo got in and the car creaked and sighed. Mr Jumbo was so very, very heavy!

"Drive slowly," said Mr Jumbo, looking round at his luggage. "I don't want any of my cases to drop off, Noddy."

So Noddy drove very slowly, and went up the little hill to Mr Jumbo's house, with the car creaking loudly.

"Your car needs oiling, Noddy," said Mr Jumbo.

"I oiled it this morning," said Noddy. He didn't like to tell Mr Jumbo that the creaking was because he was so fat and heavy! Out they got when they came to the house, and Noddy held the door open for Mr Jumbo.

"Hey – your car's beginning to run down the hill!" said Mr Jumbo in alarm.

"But I've put on the brake!" said Noddy. "It can't move!"

But all the same it *was* moving! Noddy was alarmed. Wasn't the brake holding it? No, it wasn't! Something was wrong with it, it was slipping!

"Oh, you're right! The car *is* trying to run downhill!" said Noddy. "The brake has gone wrong. Oh, dear, what shall I do?"

"Well, I want you to help me in with my luggage," said Mr Jumbo, "so you can't stand here and hold the car still. Tie it to that lamp-post. That will hold it steady while we go indoors with the luggage."

"Oh, good idea!" said Noddy, pleased, and he took out his tow-rope from the boot and tied the car to the lamp-post very tightly. "There!" he said. "Now the car will keep quite still. I'll bring in your cases at once, Mr Jumbo."

He carried them in, and then Mr Jumbo paid him. "I'll give you *three* sixpences," he said, "because you're a very *willing* little fellow, Noddy. You don't sigh and grumble when cases are heavy!"

"Oh *thank* you! *Three* sixpences! I *am* lucky!" said Noddy. He went back to his car very pleased and got in. He QUITE forgot that it was tied to the lamp-post! Oh, Noddy, Noddy!

He started up the car, singing a joyful little song.

> "One, two, three
> Sixpences for me,
> I'm rich as can be,
> With a one, two, three!"

As he drove off, the rope behind pulled the lamp-post over.

CRASH! Noddy stopped in alarm. What in the world was that? He looked behind to see, but the light had gone out when the lamp hit the ground, and Noddy couldn't see anything in the dark.

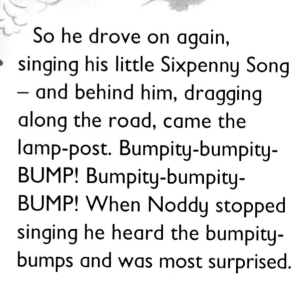

So he drove on again, singing his little Sixpenny Song – and behind him, dragging along the road, came the lamp-post. Bumpity-bumpity-BUMP! Bumpity-bumpity-BUMP! When Noddy stopped singing he heard the bumpity-bumps and was most surprised.

What was making that curious noise? He drove more slowly, and yes, there it was still. Bump-bump-bumpity-BUMP!

"Something's following me and my little car!" cried Noddy, in alarm. "Somebody's after me! Oh dear – I'd better drive to the police station and tell Mr Plod. Go away, you nasty thing behind me. I shan't stop till I get to Mr Plod!"

Noddy drove at top speed, and Mr Wobbly Man, who was just wobbling across the road, was most astonished to see Noddy whizz past, and then to be knocked over by something long and hard bumping behind the car!

"It's a good thing I'm a wobbly man and can't fall down!" he thought. "What *is* Noddy thinking of!"

And then Noddy swung round a corner, with the lamp-post bumping behind him over the pavement – and down went

someone big and heavy. It was Mr Plod the policeman.

He yelled angrily after Noddy. "What do you think you're doing, towing lamp-posts along at night! Are you mad?"

Noddy stopped when he heard Mr Plod's voice. "Oh, Mr Plod!" he called. "I was just coming to see you. Something is chasing me!"

"Yes. It looks very much like a lamp-post," said Mr Plod, grimly, picking himself up and going to the car. "That's what is chasing you, Noddy! It's tied on to your car. Now can you tell me how a lamp-post can possibly have tied itself to your car?"

"Oh, dear! Oh, Mr Plod, I tied it on myself and forgot about it!" said poor Noddy. "You see, I took Mr Jumbo and his luggage home, and something went wrong with my brake, and the car began to run down the hill, and…"

"And so you tied it to the nearest lamp-post!" said Mr Plod. "That's a very peculiar story, Noddy! I'm afraid I'll have to ask you to take me up to Mr Jumbo's house to ask him if it's true."

"Well, get in then, Mr Plod," said Noddy. "Please don't look so cross. Mr Jumbo will tell you it was *his* idea to tie the car to the lamp-post!"

Well, they were soon at Mr Jumbo's with the lamp-post still bumping behind them. Mr Plod carefully stood the lamp-post up in its place, and then they went in to see Mr Jumbo.

"Dear, dear!" said Mr Jumbo, when he heard what Mr Plod had to say. "Yes, it's quite true. I *did* suggest that Noddy should tie his car to the lamp-post. Do stay and have a cup of cocoa with me, both of you – and some biscuits. I'm so very sorry my idea caused so much trouble."

So they sat and had cocoa and

biscuits, and then Mr Plod and Noddy got into the little car again, and drove off together.

CRASH! Bumpity-bumpity-BUMP! Good gracious me, that was the *same* lamp-post falling over again. You forgot to undo the rope, Noddy – and Mr Plod forgot to remind you. Well, well, he can't scold you *this* time!

Toy Town School
with Miss Prim

Learn about moving

Something to know

In the story 'Crash! Bumpity-Bump!' Noddy helped Mr Jumbo move his luggage and also moved the lamp-post by mistake. Moving things can be very difficult. To make it easier you can fit some wheels or put a roller underneath them.

Something to understand

In the story Mr Plod was not sure that Noddy was telling the truth. Remember you should always tell the truth otherwise you might get yourself or someone else into trouble. When Mr Plod asked Mr Jumbo what had happened he was told that what Noddy said was true.

Can you think of a time when you forgot to do something? Talk to someone such as your teacher, mum, dad, brother or sister about a time when they forgot to do something important.

MISS PRIM'S NOTE FOR GROWN-UPS

Part of the Science National Curriculum deals with movement. Having the chance to try out the principle effects of force and energy is important. Discuss with the children how we move and also what makes things go. They need also to talk about their feelings and the importance of telling the truth. Listening to them is as important as speaking to them if they are to develop confidence.

Something to do

Make a slope out of a piece of wood and a pile of books. Put some of the things in the list at the top of your slope and watch how they move. Some will move better than others.

**ball   toy car
marble   cotton reel
pencil**

Dot-to-Dot

Join the dots to see who is having cocoa and biscuits with Noddy and Mr Plod. Then colour the picture.

Noddy's Car is Clever

1 One morning Noddy's car stopped. "Parp-parp," it said.

2 "You have run out of petrol!" said Noddy. "Now we are stuck!"

3 "Let me help you push," said a smiling monkey. "There is a hill."

4 "The car will run down the hill easily. Here it goes."

5 Then suddenly Monkey leapt into the car himself.

6 It raced down the hill! "He has stolen it!" cried Noddy.

7 "He will get petrol at the bottom! What shall I do?"

8 What did the car do as soon as it got petrol?

9 It raced back to Noddy! What a shock for Monkey!

Learn to Read with NODDY

Dear

My car ran out of today. A

helped to push the  . Suddenly the

monkey jumped into the as it went

down a  . The car ran down to the

 and put in some

 .Then before the could drive

away, my  raced back to me.

Wasn't it clever!

With lots of love from

NODDY

Maze

Help Noddy's little car choose the right road to get back to Noddy.

ANSWER: Road B is the road back to Noddy.

Noddy and the Broken Bicycle

Big-Ears has cycled into Mr Jumbo and fallen off and hurt his head. Mr Jumbo has sat down on the bicycle and smashed it to pieces. Only the bicycle bell is left stuck on to his tail. Noddy drives Big-Ears back to House-for-One, taking the bell with him.

Big-Ears is in bed but he is very unhappy about his bicycle.

"I'll earn enough money to get you another one," says Noddy.

Mrs Tubby Bear comes to tell Noddy that Mr Straw wants him to take some sacks to Goblin Corner.

Mr Plod thinks that Noddy stole Mr Straw's sacks. Mrs Tubby Bear tells them that a goblin gave her the message.

"The goblin is the thief, then!" cries Noddy. "I'll wait at Goblin Corner and catch whoever comes for the sacks."

That night when it is dark, Noddy goes to Goblin Wood. He hides his car in a hollow tree. Then he climbs a big tree and sits quietly, waiting for the thief. Suddenly, he hears a rustling noise below him.

Noddy peers through the branches. A hand is reaching for the sacks.

Noddy jumps right out of the tree and lands on top of a goblin!

He pulls the goblin over to his car. The car switches on its headlamps.

"Why it's Sly!" Noddy shouts. "You bad goblin! I shall take you to Mr Plod and he'll put you in prison!"

"Don't take me to Mr Plod," begs Sly. "I'll do anything you want. I can make a spell for you."

Suddenly, Noddy has a good idea. "Can you make a new bicycle for Big-Ears? He still has the bell."

"Yes, I can work a Bicycle Spell, if I have the bell," says Sly. So Noddy takes him back home. Sly puts the bell on the floor and draws a magic circle round it. Then he starts to weave his spell.

First two wheels appear, then the pedals and brakes and, finally, the tyres and handlebars. They all grow into Big-Ears' bicycle!

"My bicycle's all right again!" cries Big-Ears happily.

"You see!" says Noddy. "I said I'd get you another bicycle!"

Bell Spell

Bell, bell,
I weave you a spell,
Bicycle magic is in it.
Grow, grow,
Two wheels in a row,
It won't take you more than a minute!
Make, make,
Pedals and brake,
Tyres and handlebar too.
Bell, bell,
I weave you a spell,
Hollabee, rinnabee, HOOOOO!

Toy Town School

with Miss Prim

Something to know

In the story 'Noddy and the Broken Bicycle', Sly the Goblin was going to steal Farmer Straw's sacks. Remember that it is wrong to take something that is not yours. Luckily, Sly the Goblin was caught by Noddy before he had a chance to steal the sacks.

Something to understand

In the story Big-Ears was sad because he had run into Mr Jumbo on his bicycle and hurt himself. Noddy was very kind and came to help him. It is important to remember to help people. Sometimes if people are in difficulty they may need our help. Talk to your teacher, mum, dad, brother or sister about a time when they needed help from someone else. Lots of different people can help us, a friend, your teacher, your mum or dad, a police officer. But remember, NEVER ask for help from a stranger.

Something to do

In the story Sly the Goblin makes a new bicycle with a magic spell. Use the pieces below to draw Big-Ears' new bicycle.

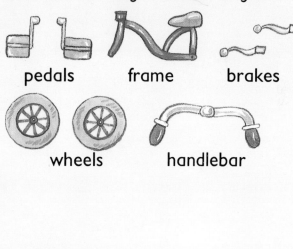

pedals   frame   brakes

wheels   handlebar

MISS PRIM'S NOTE FOR GROWN-UPS

Part of the English National Curriculum involves children in talking about characters in a story or events or activities that have happened in or out of school. Helping each other is important but at the same time children should be told about the dangers of asking for help from people they don't know.

43

The Toy Town Picnic

It's a sunny day and everyone is enjoying a picnic.
Look carefully at the objects in the border and try
to find them in the main picture.

Noddy's Silly Mistake

1 Once Noddy met Tessie Bear out shopping. She called to him.

2 "I have left Bumpy Dog tied up in the market. Please fetch him."

3 "Right," said Noddy, and off he ran. There was Bumpy Dog!

4 Noddy untied the rope, and went off. It was the wrong rope!

5 There is a cow on the end of the rope. NODDY! Stop, Noddy!

6 The cow went lumbering after Noddy. They met Tessie Bear.

7 "Here is Bumpy!" called Noddy. "It is not!" Tessie cried.

8 "He has turned into a cow! What *shall* we do?" said Noddy.

9 Oh, Noddy! Take the cow back at once – and get poor Bumpy!

Farm Fun

Noddy is helping Farmer Straw on his farm today. There are lots of animals to see. Look at the different animals and write the name of each animal in the panel next to it.

cow

hen

sheep

pig

horse

These are the words you need:
cow   hen   horse   pig   sheep

COLOUR IN WITH NODDY

"I love my little car!"

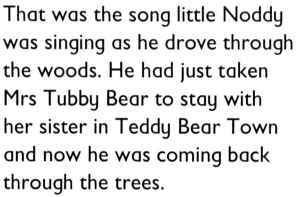

"Here I go
In my little car,
Bumpity-bump,
How happy we are!"

That was the song little Noddy was singing as he drove through the woods. He had just taken Mrs Tubby Bear to stay with her sister in Teddy Bear Town and now he was coming back through the trees.

The path was very rough – bumpity-bump went the car and Noddy bounced up and down in the driving seat.

"I feel as if I were riding on a horse!" he said. And then, quite suddenly, the little car stopped. Noddy was surprised. "What's the matter with you?" he said. "I didn't make you stop. Have you got a puncture in one of your tyres?"

"Parp-parp-parp-parp-PARP!" said the little car, as if it wanted to tell Noddy something important. Noddy wondered what it could be saying. He looked all round him – and then he suddenly heard somebody shouting.

"Oh, help, help! Oh, I shall fall! Oh, help, help!"

"Dear me – somebody's in trouble," said Noddy, and he got out of his car at once. He stood and listened. Where was the shouting coming from?

"It seems to be coming from high up," said Noddy to himself. "Perhaps it's somebody up in a tree?"

So he went to look up at the trees – and there, high up in a big tree he saw something blue. He looked and he looked, and then he saw little Connie Kitten in her blue dress.

"Connie Kitten! What's happened?" he called.

"Oh, is that you, little Noddy?" shouted Connie Kitten. "Please help me! I've climbed up this tree and I daren't get down. I just daren't!"

"Good gracious! Whatever did you climb it for then?" asked Noddy, climbing up himself.

"Well, a bird called something rude after me and I thought I would climb up to its nest and take its eggs," said Connie.

"That wasn't very nice of you," said Noddy. "You shouldn't take birds' eggs, you know that."

"Well, I wish I hadn't climbed up now," said Connie Kitten, beginning to cry. "I'm frightened. I couldn't reach the nest and now that horrid bird is laughing at me."

"Well, look – put your foot just *here*," said little Noddy, taking hold of Connie Kitten's ankle and pulling it gently down to a lower branch.

But she screamed loudly and clutched the trunk of the tree tightly. "No, no – I shall fall, I know I shall. You must carry me down."

"Don't be silly, I can't do that," said Noddy. "I'm not big enough. Look – just tread *here*, and then…"

"No!" squealed Connie Kitten. "I'm afraid of climbing down. Get somebody to come and carry me down."

"All right," said Noddy and began to climb down. "I must say that I think you are very silly, Connie Kitten."

When he was halfway down Connie squealed again. "I'm falling! I feel dizzy! I shall fall right down and hurt myself. Come back, Noddy, and hold me."

Noddy climbed back as fast as he could. Connie Kitten had her eyes closed and she certainly looked frightened! Noddy put his arm round her.

"Don't fall. Don't let go. I'm holding you. But how can I get help if I have to stay up here with you and hold you all

the time, Connie Kitten?" he said.

"I don't know," said Connie, clutching at Noddy and almost making him lose his balance. "I know I shall fall! Oh, why did I think I could climb a tree – and in my new dress, too!"

Noddy suddenly had a very good idea. He took his scarf and put it round a nearby branch – and he put it round Connie Kitten too! He knotted his nice yellow scarf tightly – and there was Connie Kitten, tied fast to a branch!

"There!" said little Noddy, pleased. "You're quite safe now, Connie. Even if you fall, the scarf will hold you up. Don't be afraid any more. I'm going to climb down and get Big-Ears, my friend, to come and rescue you. He's very strong."

"I do think you're clever, little Noddy!" said Connie.

Noddy climbed down the tree again and ran to his car. "I'll soon come back with Big-Ears!" he said, and away he went to Big-Ears' toadstool house.

Big-Ears was at home, which was lucky. "Come at once, Big-Ears!" cried Noddy. "Connie Kitten's up a tree and she can't get down! I've tied her tightly to a branch with my scarf, but she feels very, very dizzy."

"Dear me – that Connie Kitten is always getting into some fix or other!" said Big-Ears, and he got into Noddy's car. Off they went.

Noddy drove to the big tree and called loudly. "Connie Kitten! Here we are. Big-Ears is going to climb up and carry you down."

There was no answer, so Noddy called again and Big-Ears got out of the car. He peered up the tree.

"No wonder there isn't an answer!" he said. "There's nobody there. It must be the wrong tree!"

"It isn't, it isn't!" said Noddy, and he got out to look, too. But dear me, there was no Connie Kitten!

"Drive your car round and shout," said Big-Ears, rather cross. So Noddy drove round and yelled at the top of his voice. But no Connie Kitten answered.

"It was just a joke she played on you!" said Big-Ears. "She must have climbed down as soon as you had

gone, and run home laughing
– with your nice yellow scarf!"

"Goodness me – the horrid
kitten!" said Noddy in a rage.
"I'm going to Connie Kitten's
home right now to give her a
good scolding!"

And dear me, off he went in
a dreadful temper. Look out,
Connie Kitten – here comes a
very angry Noddy!

He came to Connie Kitten's
house and banged the door –
blam, blam, blam! He put a big
frown on his face, and his
head nodded very fast indeed
– nid-niddy-nod-nid-niddy-nod!

The door opened – and
there was Connie Kitten, all smiles! "Oh, it's
you, Noddy! I was just ironing your scarf,
ready to bring it back to you, it was so
crumpled with knots. My uncle, Mr Whiskers
Cat, came by just after you had gone, and
untied me and lifted me down."

"Oh," said Noddy, and his frown flew off his
face at once.

"I thought perhaps you had been playing a
horrid trick on me, Connie Kitten."

"Oh *no*! I just wanted to iron your scarf –
and look, I bought you a nice little scarf-pin on
my way back," said Connie, showing him a
beautiful scarf-pin. "I was going to call at your
house and leave them for you. Oh, Noddy, I

do think you are clever – nobody else but you would ever have thought of tying me to the tree with a scarf!"

Noddy was very, very pleased. "I was going to be cross and scold you," he said, "but now I am pleased and I want to buy you an ice-cream. Get into my car and we'll go."

"Put your scarf on first," said Connie, and he put it on and proudly put in his new scarf-pin. Off they go – and I can hear him singing his little song!

"Here we go
In my little car,
Bumpity-bump,
How happy we are!"

Noddy Says!

How much do you remember? Give yourself a nod for each answer you get right.

- Who did Noddy see up in the tree?
- What did Noddy use his scarf for?
- Whom did Noddy ask for help?
- What nice present did Connie Kitten give to Noddy?

COLOUR IN WITH NODDY

"I'm glad I remembered my umbrella!"

Toy Town School
with Miss Prim

Learn about trees

Something to know

In the story 'Noddy Climbs a Tree' he very bravely climbed a tree to rescue Connie Kitten. But Connie was scared of climbing down. Noddy almost fell out of the tree when he went to help her. Trees can grow very tall. They are the largest of all plants. When Noddy climbed up into the tree he found that Connie was caught on one of the branches. The branches grow out of the trunk of the tree. Twigs grow from the branches and leaves grow from the twigs.

Connie was caught up in a tall tree. Some trees such as an oak and a beech can grow very large.

Something to do

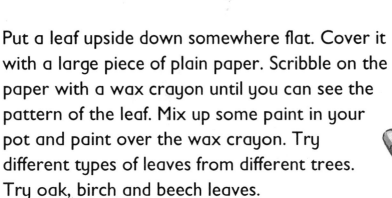

You will need
wax crayons   plain paper
water based paints
paintbrush   pot

Put a leaf upside down somewhere flat. Cover it with a large piece of plain paper. Scribble on the paper with a wax crayon until you can see the pattern of the leaf. Mix up some paint in your pot and paint over the wax crayon. Try different types of leaves from different trees. Try oak, birch and beech leaves.

Something to understand

When Noddy was climbing the tree he went up the trunk and along the branches. Each part of the tree has a different name. Look at the words and fit them into the correct boxes below.

**leaves   branch   trunk
roots   twig**

Never climb up a tree as it could be very dangerous and you could get stuck just like Connie.

Spot the Difference

These two pictures are not quite the same. Have a close look at both pictures – there are five differences in picture 2 for you to spot.

Answers: 1. Noddy's hat is a different colour. 2. The ladybird is missing 3 The door of Big-Ears' toadstool house is a different colour. 4. Bumpy Dog's collar is missing 5. Big-Ears' hat is missing.

Good Night

"It's dark and it's quiet,
I'm going to sleep.
My eyes are tight shut,
They can't even peep.
I'll dream of Old Big-Ears,
And dear Tessie Bear.
I'm going to Dreamland,
And now
I
Am
THERE!"

61

NODDY TOYS TO WIN!

You could be one of 21 lucky Noddy Annual readers to win a special Noddy prize!

How would you like to play in a Dekkertoys Playhouse just like Noddy's? It is made of strong plastic printed with pictures of Noddy and Big-Ears, and it is so big that you can play inside it. We have 10 to send to lucky winners!

The Noddy Toy Town House from Dekkertoys is just as much fun. It has play figures of Noddy and Big-Ears, a garage with doors that open, and of course a Noddy car. We have 5 to send to lucky boys and girls!